THE TIME MACHINE SERIES

LEONARD AND HIS TIME MACHINE

GENE DARBY

LEONARD VISITS THE OCEAN FLOOR

ILLUSTRATED BY RIC HUGO

Addison-Wesley Publishing Company, Inc.
Menlo Park, California • Reading, Massachusetts • London • Amsterdam
Don Mills, Ontario • Sydney

TABLE of CONTENTS

ISBN 0-201-40602-0
ABCDEFGHIJ-WZ-807987

UP AND AWAY

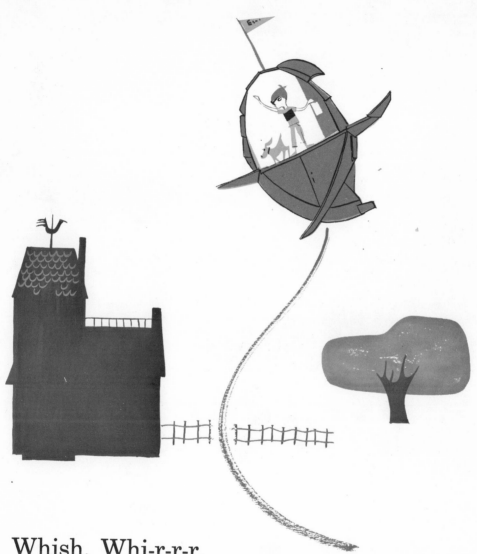

Whish. Whi-r-r-r.

Up and away.

Away went Leonard in the time machine.

He went back in time.
He went back . . . . .

back . . . . .

back . . . . .

back . . . . .

He went back to 1930.

Leonard saw a boat.

Leonard saw a deep-sea diver
on the boat.

The deep-sea diver
was getting ready to go underwater.

Leonard wanted to go underwater.

The time machine came down.
The time machine came down
on the boat.

Leonard went to the deep-sea diver.
"I want to go underwater,"
said Leonard.

"Get ready," said the deep-sea diver.
"Get ready to go underwater."

The deep-sea diver was ready.
"Ready," said the deep-sea diver.

Leonard was ready to go underwater.
"Ready," said Leonard.

A big ball was on the boat.

"Get the big ball ready,"
said the deep-sea diver.

"Get the big ball ready,"
he said to the man.

9

The man worked.

Up, up, up.

Then . . . . .
Bang! Bang! Bang!
Bang! Bang! Bang!
The big ball was ready.

Away went the big ball.
Away went the time machine.

"Oh, oh, oh," said the deep-sea diver.
"I see underwater."

"Wow!" said Leonard.

14

LOOK! LOOK!

The big ball was in the water.
Down went the deep-sea diver.

Down . . . . .

Down . . . . .

Down . . . . .

A big octopus came.
A big octopus saw the big ball.

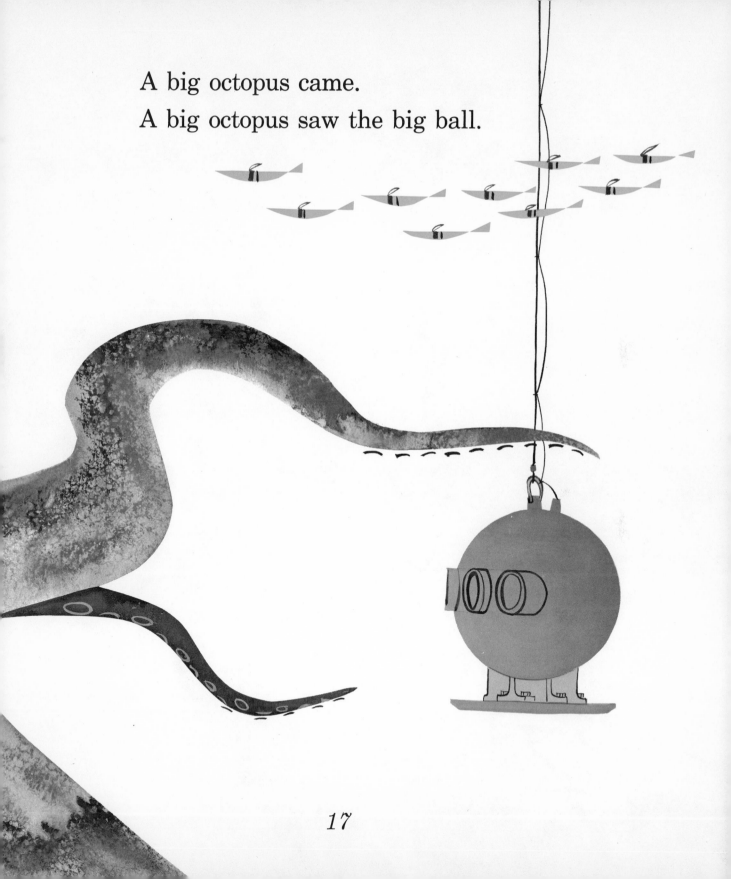

The deep-sea diver saw the octopus.

Leonard saw the octopus.

Leonard wanted the octopus
to go away.

The octopus went away.

Swim, swim, swim.

Down . . . . .

Down . . . . .

Down went the big ball.
Then, "Oh, oh, oh!"

"Help! Help!" said the deep-sea diver.

Leonard wanted to help.

"Leonard to deep-sea diver," said Leonard.

"Leonard to deep-sea diver.

Here I come to help.

Here I come to help."

Leonard went down to help.

Up came the big ball.
Up, up, up.

FISH! FISH!

"Leonard to deep-sea diver.
Leonard to deep-sea diver.
I see fish coming.
I see fish coming," said Leonard.

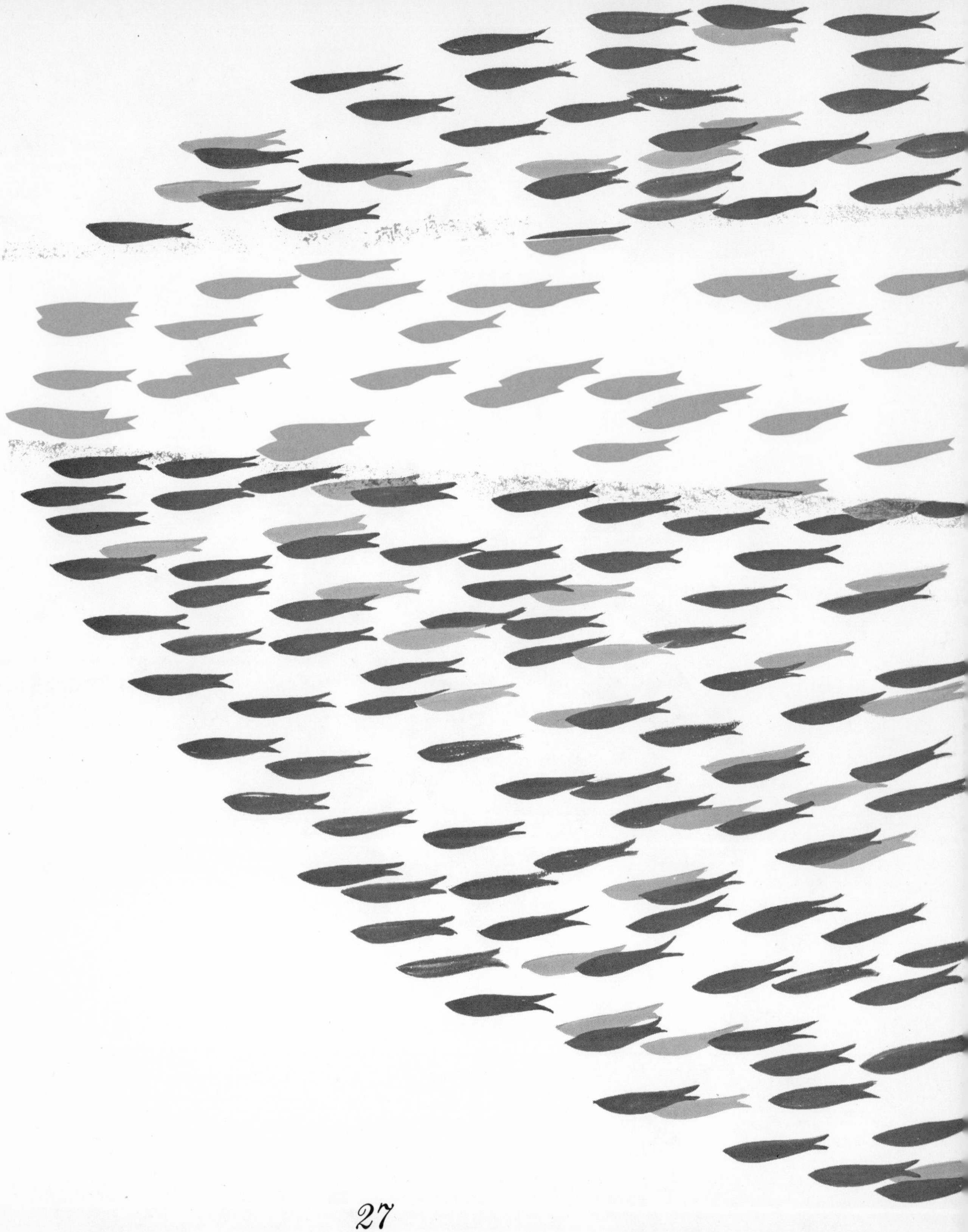

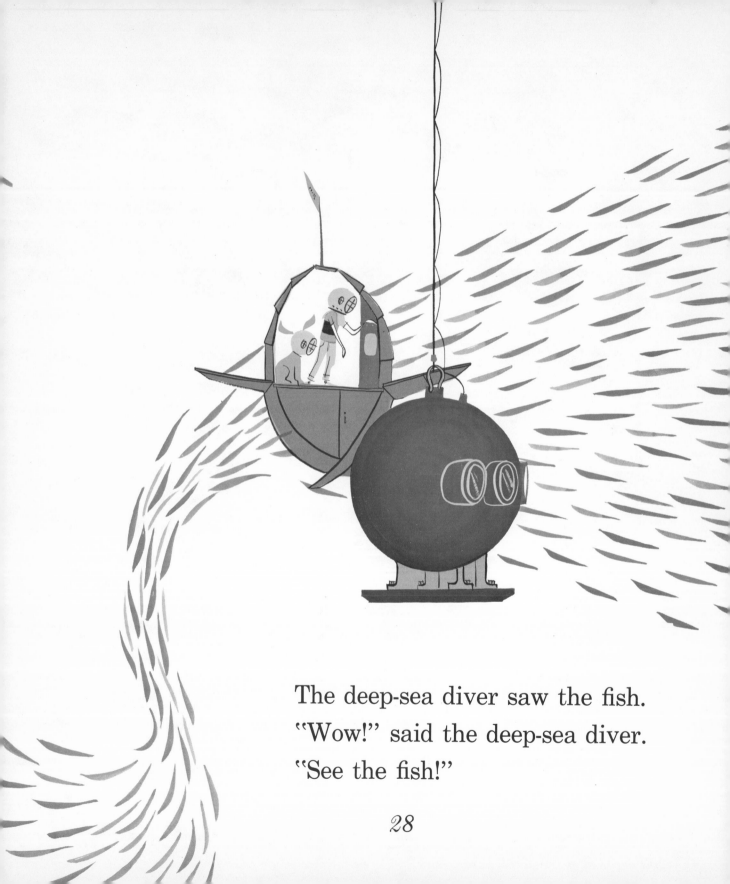

The deep-sea diver saw the fish.
"Wow!" said the deep-sea diver.
"See the fish!"

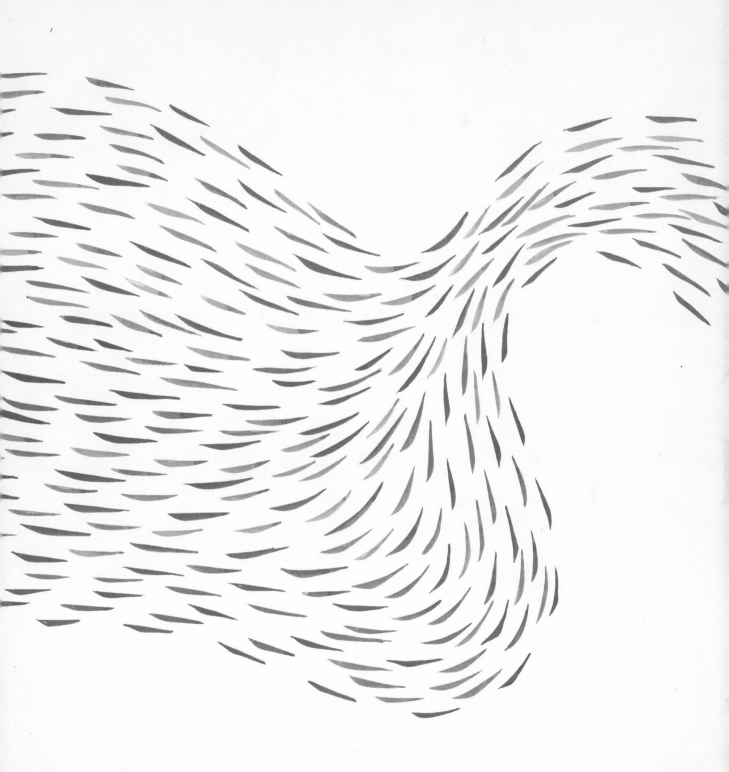

29

Then more fish came . . . . .

And more fish came.

Then more fish came . . . . .

And more fish came.

Swim, swim, swim came the fish.

"Leonard to deep-sea diver.
Leonard to deep-sea diver.
Look! Look!
Look and see!" said Leonard.
"Here come more fish."

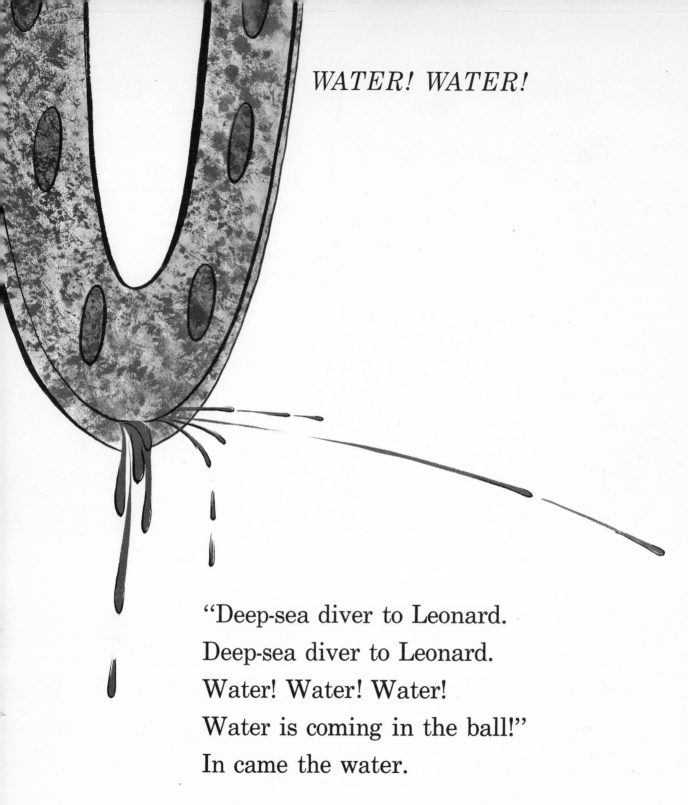

WATER! WATER!

"Deep-sea diver to Leonard.
Deep-sea diver to Leonard.
Water! Water! Water!
Water is coming in the ball!"
In came the water.

It came in the ball.
In . . . . in . . . . in . . . . .

"Oh!" said the deep-sea diver.
"I want to go up.
I want to go up to the boat."

"Up," said the man on the boat.
"Come up, big ball.
Come up, deep-sea diver.
Come up."

Then the big ball went around.
It went around and around.

It went around

and around

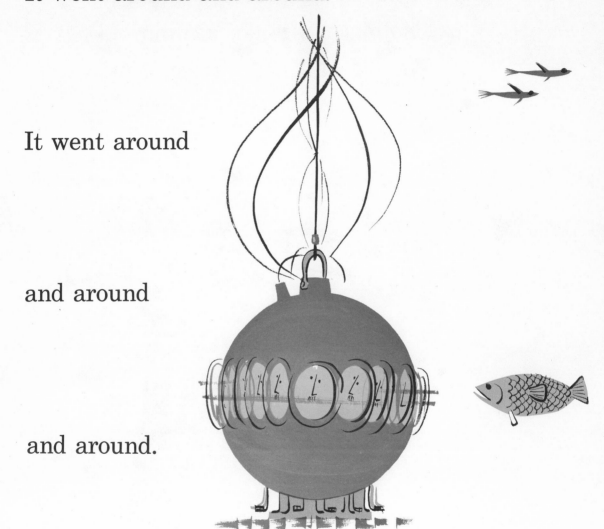

and around.

"The ball is not going up,"
said the deep-sea diver.

"Oh!" said the man on the boat.
"The big ball is not coming up!
The big ball is not coming up!
The big ball is not coming up!"

"Oh," said Leonard.
"The big ball is not going up."

"Leonard to deep-sea diver.
Leonard to deep-sea diver.
Here I come.
Here I come," said Leonard.

Leonard worked.

He worked and he worked.

He worked and worked and worked.

Then, up went the big ball.

It went up to the boat.

It went up to the man on the boat.

Up, up, up went the time machine.

"It is time to go," said Leonard.
"It is time to go."

And away he went.

"Look," said Leonard.

"Here I come."

"I was a deep-sea diver,"
said Leonard.

WORD LIST

Leonard Visits the Ocean Floor uses a vocabulary of 49 different words for a total of 581 running words. The entire vocabulary is listed below. Following each word is the number of the page on which it first appears.

a	4	down	5	look	15	see	13
and	1					swim	19
around	37	fish	26	machine	1		
away	1			man	9	the	1
		get	4	more	30	then	11
back	2	go	4			time	1
ball	9			not	37	to	3
bang	11	he	2				
big	9	help	20	octopus	17	underwater	4
boat	4	here	22	oh	13	up	1
				on	4		
		I	6			want	4
came	5	in	1			was	4
come	22	is	34	ready	4	water	15
		it	35			went	1
deep-sea	4			said	6	worked	10
diver	4	Leonard	1	saw	4		